BANKSY COLOURING
& DRAWING BOOK

BY MARTIN BULL

THIS BOOK BELONGS TO

NAME - ....

CLASS - ....

For Kai & Butu

Long may you colour and draw as children and as adults

ENJOY,

M 2024

Banksy Colouring & Drawing Book
First Edition
Published in the Independent Peoples' Republic of Wiltshire by shellshock publishing
© Martin Bull 2015
ISBN 978-0-9554712-7-8

Print management by Sam @ TU Ink - www.tuink.co.uk

Printed on UPM Fine 150gsm paper from sustainable forests, holding both the FSC & EU Eco-Label Certifications.

This book was NOT printed in China, and hopefully none from shellshock publishing ever will be, despite rather tempting prices. This book was actually printed in lovely Aberystwyth, by Cambrian Printers, a splendid old independent printer.

INTRODUCTION

My previous books about the street work of Banksy have been aimed at showing readers where the pieces are and encouraging you to visit them in person.

The beauty of this book is that now you don't even have to visit the pieces in real life to feel a part of them, as drawing / colouring them can impart the close affection that art huggers like me experience when hunting down and embracing a Banksy street piece. And unlike us, you will certainly survive the skankier locations without catching a contagious disease.

Although this book was originally meant for adults, and obviously a shameless cash-in on the 'mindfulness' buzz word that is sweeping the nation, I rapidly realised that by taking out a copper sniffing a white line, and a few other images that may get the knickers in a twist of already stressed and flustered parents, it can merrily be enjoyed by children as well.

As kids we all loved to colour and draw. Yet as we 'mature' it is knocked out of us and in fact disparaged as something that is merely 'child-like'. Like most oft repeated Internet quotes Pablo Picasso may never have actually uttered the fabled line, "Every child is an artist. The problem is how to remain an artist once we grow up", but however it was formed the sentiment is perfect. I hope in its own little way this book will unlock a few inner artists amongst us adults.

Since 2007 I have donated £34,723 to charities through sales of my Banksy books and related fundraising initiatives, and I will donate 10% of any profits from this book to Bristol Mind (UK registered charity no. 1085171). They do excellent work to provide a range of high quality services which are reflective and relevant to the needs of the mental health service user community around the Bristol area. They also combat stigma and promote a positive image of mental health. Mental and emotional health problems can happen to anyone, at any age, or from any background.

I truly believe that ALL of us are just a few bad turns in life away from needing this type of help. Don't kid yourself that it couldn't be you - divorce, bereavement, redundancy, negativity, unaffordable house prices, abuse, repossession, etc can effect any of us, and it is often problems like those that lead to mental distress. Please visit - www.bristolmind.org.uk for more info.

Martin Bull

Creative Activities - 1 to 14

KEY: COLOUR DRAW A SLICE OF BOTH

1 - IKEA PUNK - 2009

2 TO 4 - A MEDLEY OF RATS - ALL CIRCA 2001-2004

5 - CRAZY BEAT - 2003

6 - PLACARD RAT - 2003/4

7 - GIANT RAT - 2004

8 - DESIGNATED PICNIC AREA - EARLY 2000'S

9 - TESCO FLAG - 2008

10 - IF GRAFFITI ... - 2011

11 - BANKSY 'HOLLOW' & ARTIST - 2007

12 - BUBBLE GIRL - 2008

13 - TAP PHONED - 2011

14 - GCHQ SNOOPERS - 2014

15 - HARING DOG & HOODIE - 2010

16 - THIS IS NOT A PHOTO OPPORTUNITY - 2002/3

17 - DESIGNATED GRAFFITI AREA - 2001

18 - FLOWER - 2007

19 - GIRL WITH BALLOON - EARLY 2000'S

20 - TESCO SANDCASTLES - 2010

21 - QUAKATTACK - CIRCA 1997

22 - NO FUTURE - 2010

23 - THE MILD MILD WEST - 1999

24 - THE NEW POLLUTION / PURE CLASS - 1997

25 - CASTLES IN THE SKY - 2011

26 - WHAT? - 2006

Creative Activities - 27 to 40

27 - GRAFFITI REMOVAL HOTLINE - 2006

28 - I ♥ NY - 2008

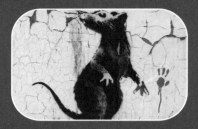

29 TO 31 - ANOTHER TRIUMVIRATE OF RATS

32 - B-BOY - 2009

33 - LAST GRAFFITI BEFORE MOTORWAY - 2009

34 - HOXTON MAID - 2006

35 - I HATE THIS FONT - 2012

36 - TOX - 2011

37 - SWEATSHOP BUNTING BOY - 2012

38 - FLOWER GIRL - 2011

39 - CATS & DOGS (DETAIL) - CIRCA 1998

40 - ONE NATION UNDER CCTV - 2008

41 - OLD SKOOL / THUGS FOR LIFE - 2004

42 - ARTISTE - 2007

43 - VISUAL WARFARE (DETAIL) - WITH KATO - 1998

44 - VOTE LESS - 2005

45 - GO BACK TO BED - CIRCA 2004

46 - FLIES (DETAIL) - 1998/9

47 - GLOBAL WARMING - 2009

48 - GORILLA - 2007

49 - BOXHEAD - 2010

50 - HMV (PLUS STYLO) - 2001

51 - CAVE PAINTING / CANS FESTIVAL BUFFER - 2008

52 - CASH MACHINE & GIRL - 2005

TWO WARM-UP PAGES

STRETCH YOUR FINGERS, CRACK YOUR KNUCKLES
& BEND YOUR MIND. LET'S GET CREATIVE...

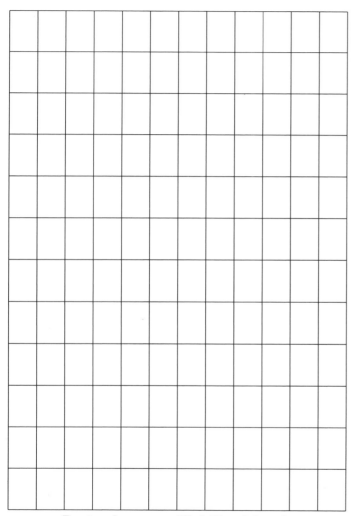

Pretend you are Piet Mondrian & create your own De Stijl masterpiece

TWO WARM-UP PAGES

COLOUR IN THE GRID, DRAW MORE STARS, SKETCH A DINOSAUR EATING A CREAM CAKE, & LET'S GET READY TO RUMBLE... ERR... OR TO COLOUR & DRAW

2-4

"I'd been painting rats for three years before someone said 'that's clever, it's an anagram of art' and I had to pretend I'd known that all along"

[Banksy - Wall & Piece - 2005]

"I am enough of the artist to draw freely upon my imagination. Imagination is more important than knowledge. Knowledge is limited. Imagination encircles the world." [Albert Einstein - 1929]

PLACARD RAT -
BARBICAN, LONDON - 2003/4

LONDON
Doesn't
work

6

"You can win the rat race but you're still a rat." [Banksy - Wall & Piece - 2005, but has been in use since at least 1956]

GIANT RAT - LIVERPOOL - 2004

IT HONESTLY IS A RAT, NOT A CAT, OR A CAT RAT

7

DESIGNATED PICNIC AREA –
SHOREDITCH, LONDON – EARLY 2000'S

DRAW YOUR OWN SCENE OF URBAN DECAY & THE WORST PLACE IN LONDON TO EVER HAVE A PICNIC

"There are truths which are not for all men, nor for all times" [Voltaire - 1764]

TESCO FLAG - ISLINGTON, LONDON - MARCH 2008

9

IF... - FITZROVIA, LONDON - APRIL 2011
PRESUMABLY A TAKE ON EMMA GOLDMAN'S
OLD ANARCHIST SLOGAN "IF VOTING CHANGED
ANYTHING, THEY'D MAKE IT ILLEGAL".

IF GRAFFITI CHANGED ANYTHING -IT WOULD BE ILLEGAL

"I tell myself I use art to promote dissent, but maybe I am just using dissent to promote my art. I plead not guilty to selling out.
But I plead it from a bigger house than I used to live in." [Banksy - Interview with Time Out London - 1st March 2010]

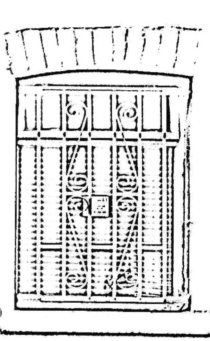

BUBBLE GIRL - HACKNEY, LONDON - FEB 2008

12

"Some mothers will do anything for their children, except let them be themselves." [Banksy - Cut It Out - 2004]

TAP PHONED - POPLAR, LONDON - AUGUST 2011

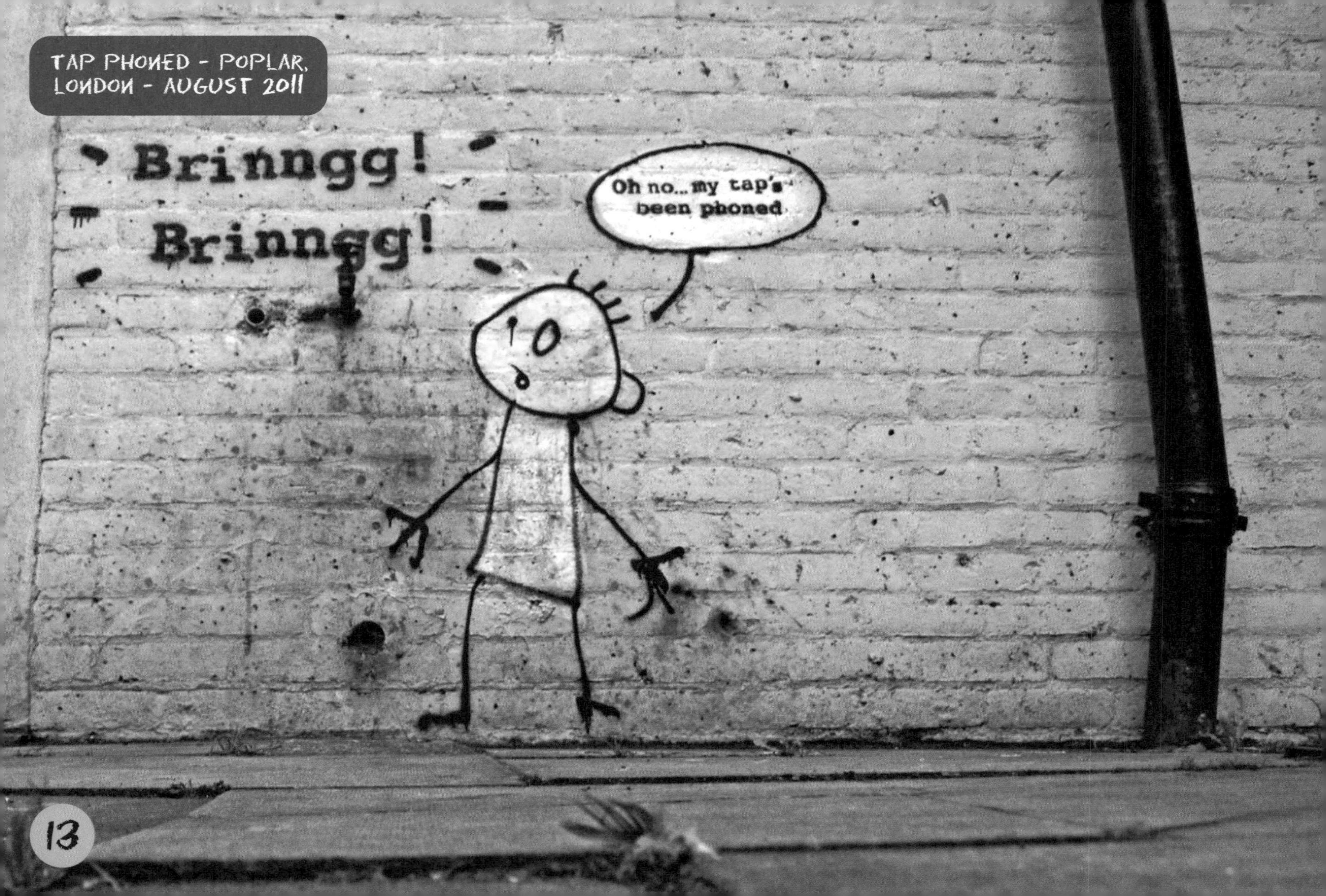

I DON'T WISH TO BE NEGATIVE, BUT TBH IF YOU CAN'T COPY THIS ONE MAYBE YOU NEED A REFUND? ☺

"All artists are willing to suffer for their work. But why are so few prepared to learn to draw?"   [Banksy - Existencilism - 2002]

15

"If you love those loving you, of what credit is it to you? For even the sinners love those loving them" [Luke's Gospel - ch 6, verse 32]

THIS IS NOT A PHOTO OPPORTUNITY
- SOUTH BANK, LONDON - 2002/3

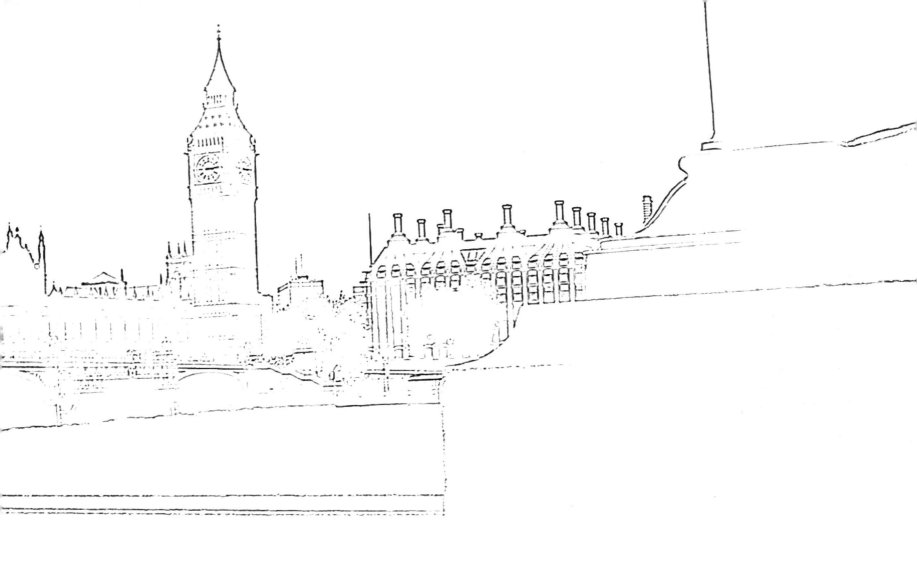

"Tourism is not a spectator sport" [Banksy, in reference to this exact street piece - Wall & Piece - 2005]

17

BY ORDER
NATIONAL HIGHWAYS AGENCY

THIS WALL IS A DESIGNATED
GRAFFITI AREA

PLEASE TAKE YOUR LITTER HOME
EC. REF. URBA 23/366

DESIGNATED GRAFFITI AREA -
SHOREDITCH, LONDON - 2001

COMPLETE THE SCENE WITH YOUR OWN KILLER POODLE.
MURDEROUS MEERKATS, SLOTHS, OR FRUIT FLIES ALSO ACCEPTED

"I write what I like" [Frank Talk, a.k.a. Steve Biko]

FLOWER - BETHNAL GREEN, LONDON - OCT 2007

18

POLLARD STREET E2

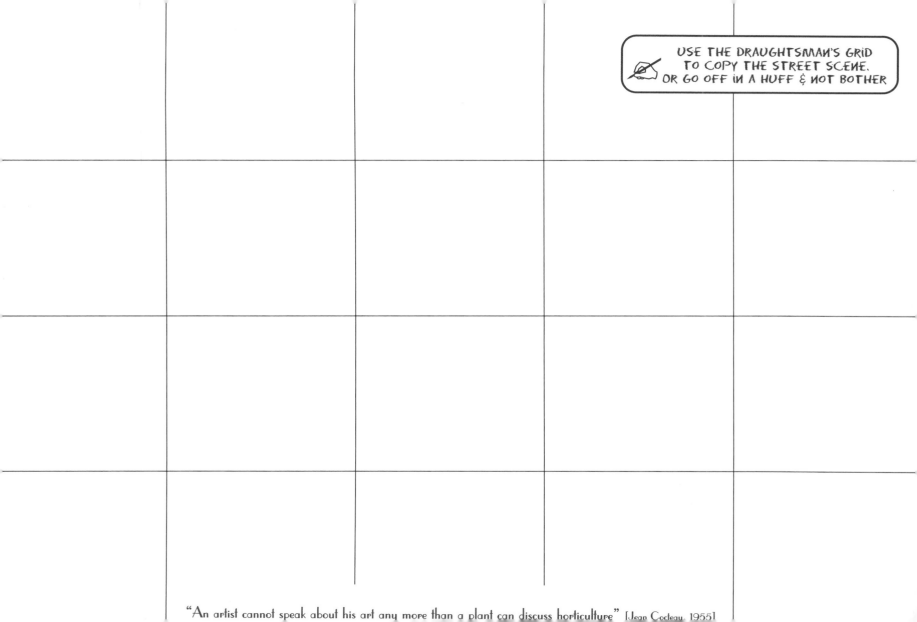

USE THE DRAUGHTSMAN'S GRID
TO COPY THE STREET SCENE.
OR GO OFF IN A HUFF & NOT BOTHER

"An artist cannot speak about his art any more than a plant can discuss horticulture" [Jean Cocteau. 1955]

"When the time comes to leave, just walk away quietly and don't make any fuss"   [Banksy, on this art piece, 2005]

DRAW & COLOUR YOUR OWN CHEESY ENGLISH SEASIDE SCENE, COMPLETE WITH PRESCIENT ANTI-CONSUMER-IST GRAFFITI, RIP-OFF ICE CREAM SELLER, SUN BURNT STICK MEN (IF YOU CAN'T DRAW PEOPLE; WHO CAN?) AND A FERAL FLOCK OF BABY SNATCHING SKYRATS.

"Cassius Clay is a slave name. I didn't choose it, and I didn't want it" [Muhammad Ali - 1964]

NO FUTURE
SOUTHAMPTON - SEPT 2010

"I knew my pictures had a message, but what it was precisely I couldn't have said - except, perhaps, that I wanted to break the hearts and spirits of secure people"

[Don McCullin - 1990]

THE MILD MILD WEST
BRISTOL - EARLY 1999

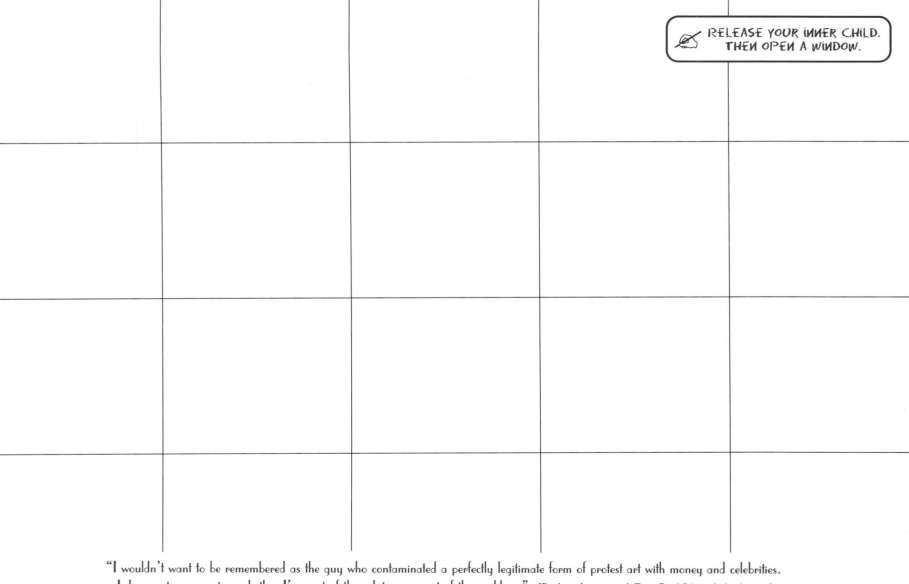

RELEASE YOUR INNER CHILD.
THEN OPEN A WINDOW.

"I wouldn't want to be remembered as the guy who contaminated a perfectly legitimate form of protest art with money and celebrities. I do sometimes question whether I'm part of the solution or part of the problem."   [Banksy - Interview with Time Out NY - 12th April 2010]

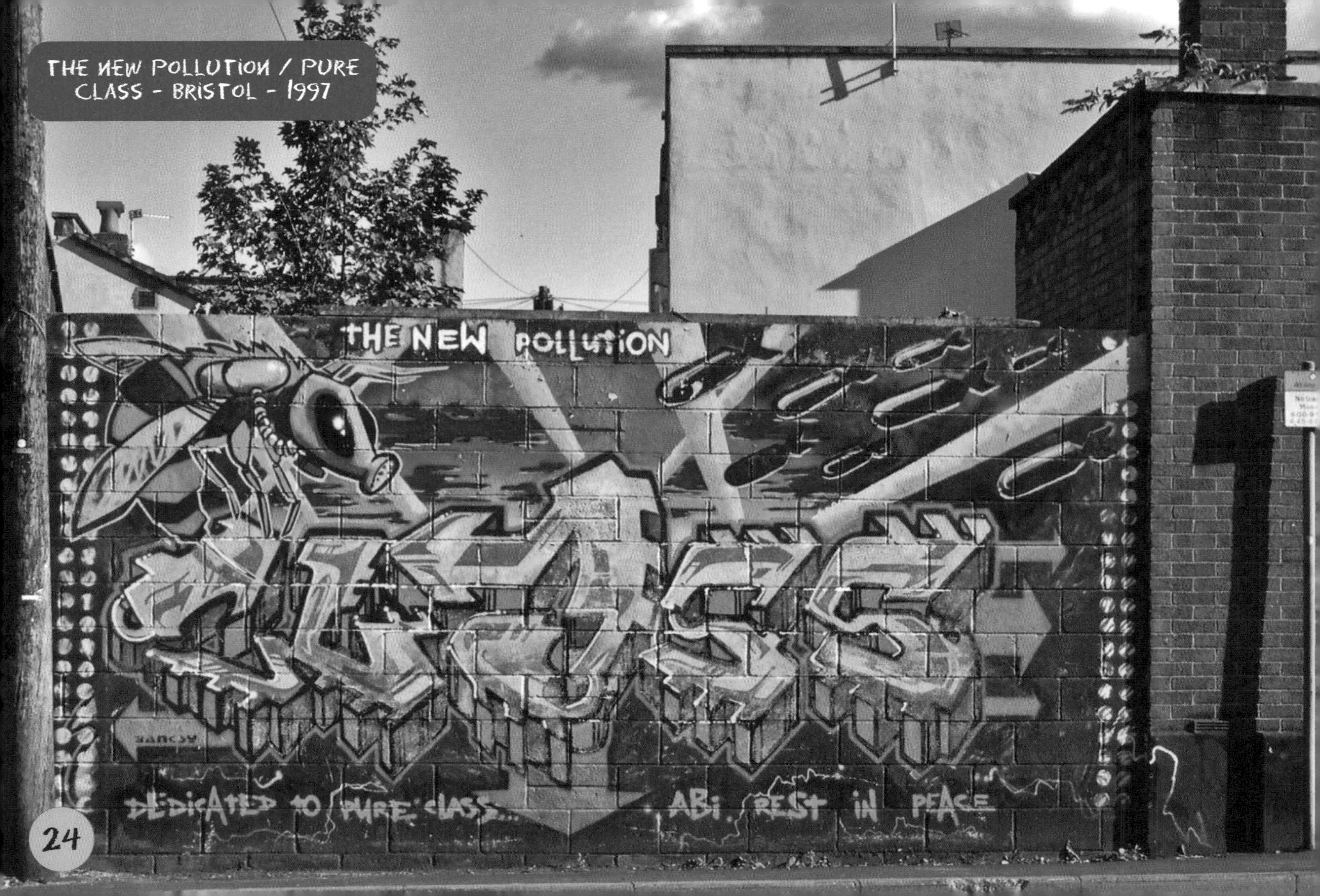

THE NEW POLLUTION / PURE CLASS - BRISTOL - 1997

CASTLES IN THE SKY
BRISTOL - DEC 2011

YOU DON'T NEED PLANNING PERMISSION TO BUILD CASTLES IN THE SKY

DRAW YOUR OWN BRICK WALL & SLOGAN —
I WILL BE COMING AROUND THE CLASS
& MARKING YOUR EFFORTS LATER...

"A wall is a very big weapon. It's one of the nastiest things you can hit someone with." [Banksy - Banging Your Head Against a Brick Wall - 2001]

"If I could say it in words there would be no reason to paint" [Edward Hopper]

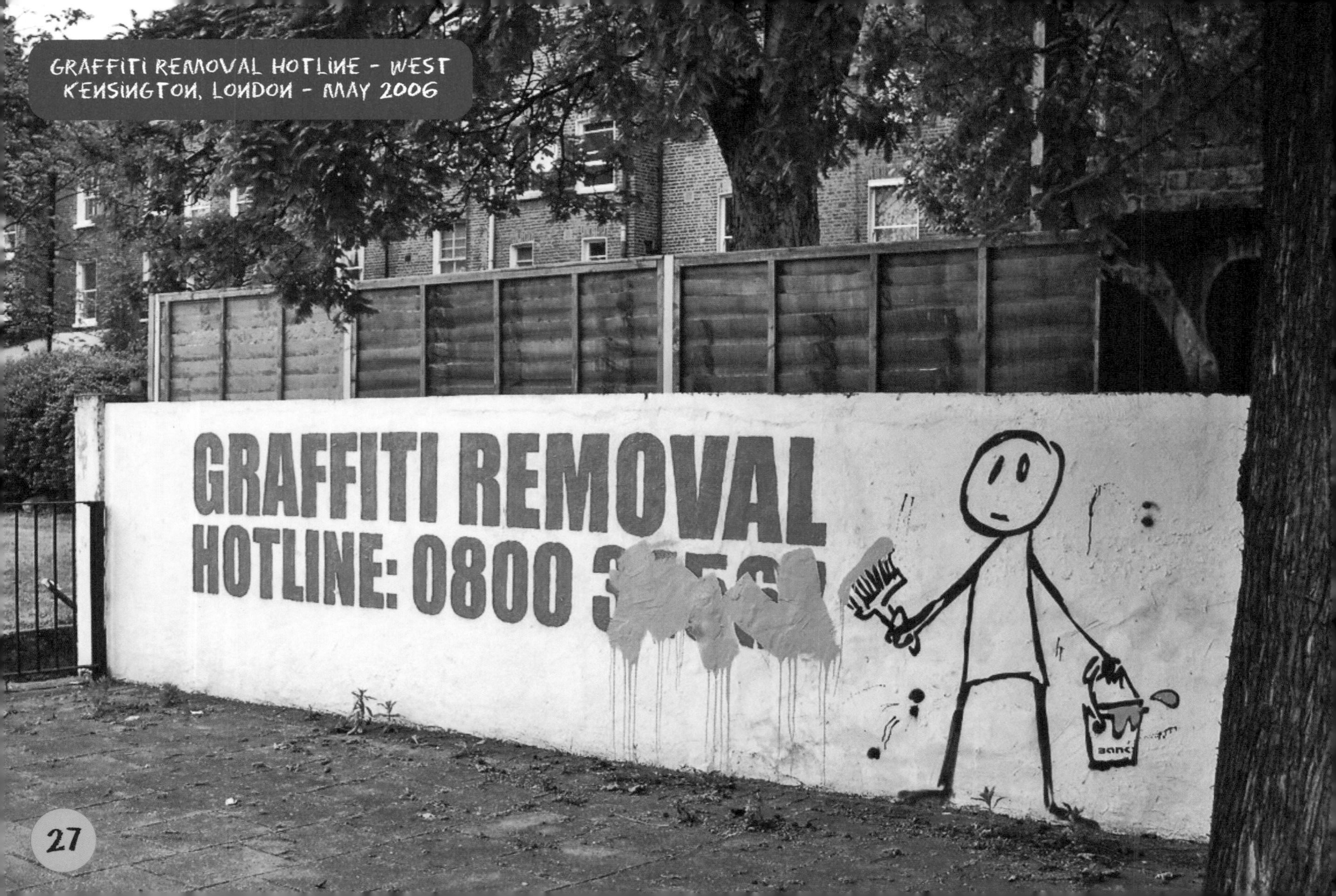

GRAFFITI REMOVAL HOTLINE - WEST KENSINGTON, LONDON - MAY 2006

"Malheur à ceux qui bâillonnent le peuple!" / "Misfortune to those who gag the people!" [Thomas Sankara - 1982]

28

29
-31

CLOCKWISE FROM ABOVE
• BETHNAL GREEN - EARLY 2000'S
• BARBICAN - CIRCA 2004
• FITZROVIA - APRIL 2011

"They exist without permission. They are hated, hunted and persecuted. They live in quiet desperation amongst the filth. And yet they are capable of bringing entire civilizations to their knees. If you are dirty, insignificant and unloved then rats are the ultimate role model."   [Banksy - Wall & Piece - 2005]

Any person who unlawfully deposits or
abandons rubbish within this area
may be prosecuted and on conviction
be liable to a fine not exceeding £1,000

The Chief Executive

"An intellectual is a man who says a simple thing in a difficult way; an artist is a man who says a difficult thing in a simple way" [Charles Bukowski - 1969]

33

MAID - HOXTON, LONDON - MAY 2006

34

"We of Africa protest that, in this day and age, we should continue to be treated as lesser human beings than other races." [Robert Mugabe - 2005]

TRY TO RIVAL MY ARTISTIC PHOTO (OOH MY
BACK) BY SKETCHING A RUN DOWN INDUSTRIAL
ESTATE & SARDONIC IN-JOKE AIMED AT TOYS
(VERY AMATEUR GRAFFITI WRITERS)

"Should graffiti be judged on the same level as modern art? Of course not: It's *way* more important than that." [Banksy - Interview with Time Out NY - 12th April 2010]

TOX – CAMDEN, LONDON – JUNE 2011

TOX WAS AN INFAMOUS ALL CITY TAGGER WHO WAS APPARENTLY JAILED FOR 27 MONTHS FOR GRAFFITI 'CRIMES'. I WRITE 'APPARENTLY' AS IT IS NOT MY PLACE TO CONFIRM OR DENY THAT THEY REALLY DID GET TOX.

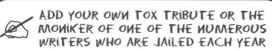

"A wall has always been the best place to publish your work"   [Banksy - Wall & Piece - 2005]

SWEATSHOP BUNTING BOY - WOOD GREEN, LONDON - MAY 2012

37

Thought for the day - When I get to any new Banksy piece why is there always a straggle haired man gurning at it? [M. R. Bull, 2012]

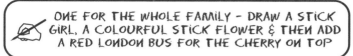

ONE FOR THE WHOLE FAMILY - DRAW A STICK GIRL, A COLOURFUL STICK FLOWER & THEN ADD A RED LONDON BUS FOR THE CHERRY ON TOP

"It took me four years to paint like Raphael, but a lifetime to paint like a child" [Pablo Picasso]

39

" there are crimes that become innocent and even glorious through their splendour number and excess"

CATS & DOGS - BRISTOL - CIRCA 1998
BANKSY'S SECTION OF A LARGER MURAL

"It is unspeakable, godless, hopeless. I am no longer an artist interested and curious, I am a messenger who will bring back word from the men who are fighting to those who want the war to go on forever. Feeble, inarticulate will be my message, but it will have a bitter truth and may it burn their lousy souls." [Paul Nash on WWI in 1917]

OLD SKOOL / THUGS FOR LIFE
CLERKENWELL, LONDON – 2004

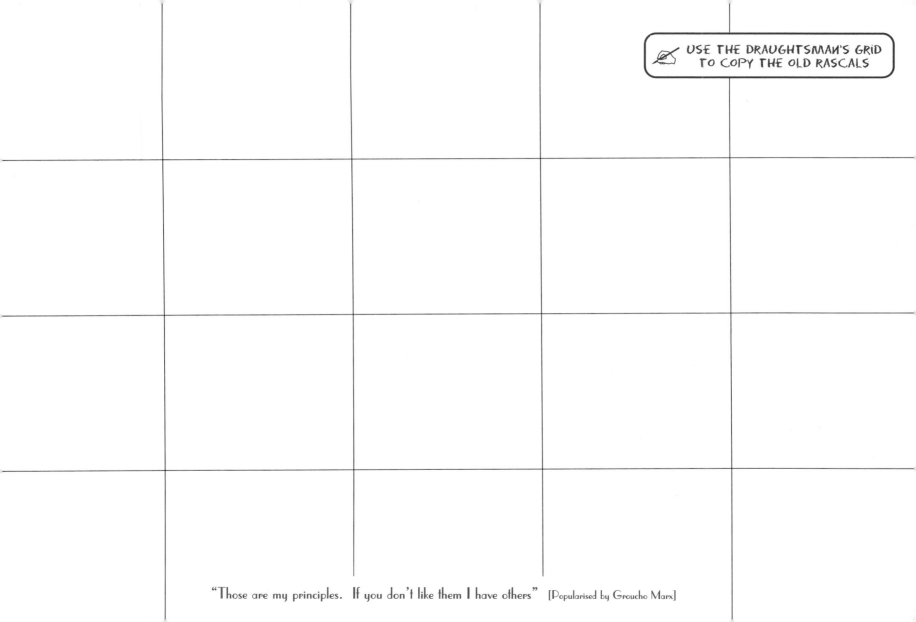

USE THE DRAUGHTSMAN'S GRID
TO COPY THE OLD RASCALS

"Those are my principles. If you don't like them I have others" [Popularised by Groucho Marx]

42

ARTISTE - SOUTH HACKNEY,
LONDON - AUG 2007

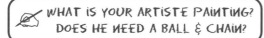

43

CLIK!

CLACK!

VISUAL WARFARE

(PART OF) VISUAL WARFARE, WITH
KATO - BRISTOL - CIRCA 1998

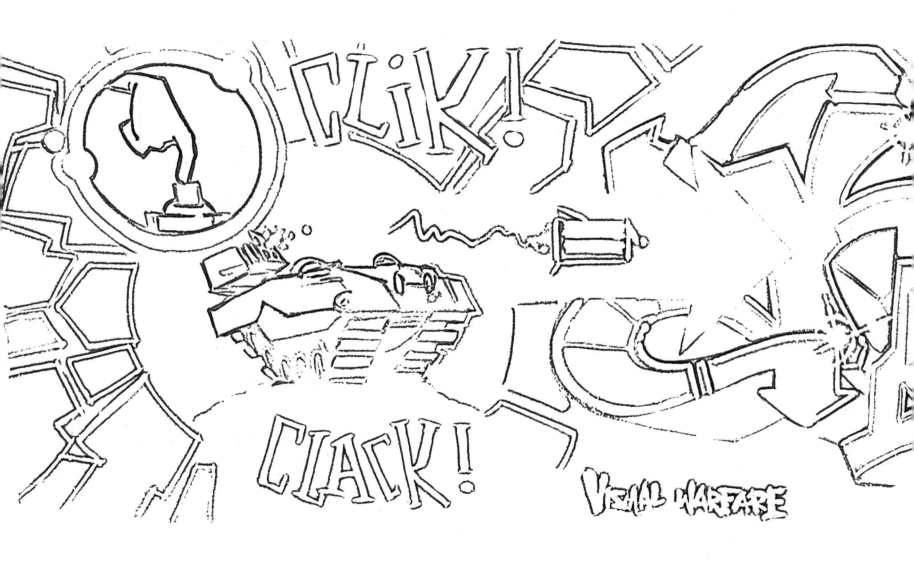

"I've never been able to paint what I set out to paint" [Edward Hopper]

VOTE LESS
BRIGHTON - 2005

DRAW YOUR OWN MAOIST /
COMMUNIST ELEPHANT
& PITHY PLACARD SLOGAN

"People seem to think if they dress like a revolutionary they don't actually have to behave like one."   [Banksy - Cut It Out - 2004]

"Un bon mot ne prouve rien" / "A witty saying proves nothing"   [Voltaire - 1767]

MY LATE FATHER USED
TO SAY A DAY WASN'T TRULY
COMPLETE UNTIL YOU'D
COLOURED IN A BUNCH OF
FLOWERS AND SOME
STICKY FLY TONGUES

"Graffiti has been used to start revolutions, stop wars, and generally is the voice of people who aren't listened to. Graffiti is one of the few tools you have if you have almost nothing." [Banksy - Banging Your Head Against a Brick Wall - 2001]

49

GIVE A KID A POSH ROBOT IN A BOX & HE'LL STILL END UP WITH THE BOX ON HIS HEAD. CLEAN CYCLISTS ARE HARD TO FIND SO I'VE OUTLINED ONE FOR YOU.

"A lot of people never use their initiative because no-one told them to." [Banksy - Banging Your Head Against a Brick Wall - 2001]

- SHOREDITCH, LONDON -

- WITH LATER ADDITIONS BY STYLO

"Speak softly, but carry a big can of paint." [Banksy - Wall & Piece - 2005]

"[Every four year old] should know that it is always OK to paint the sky orange and give cats six legs" [Alicia Bayer - 2002]

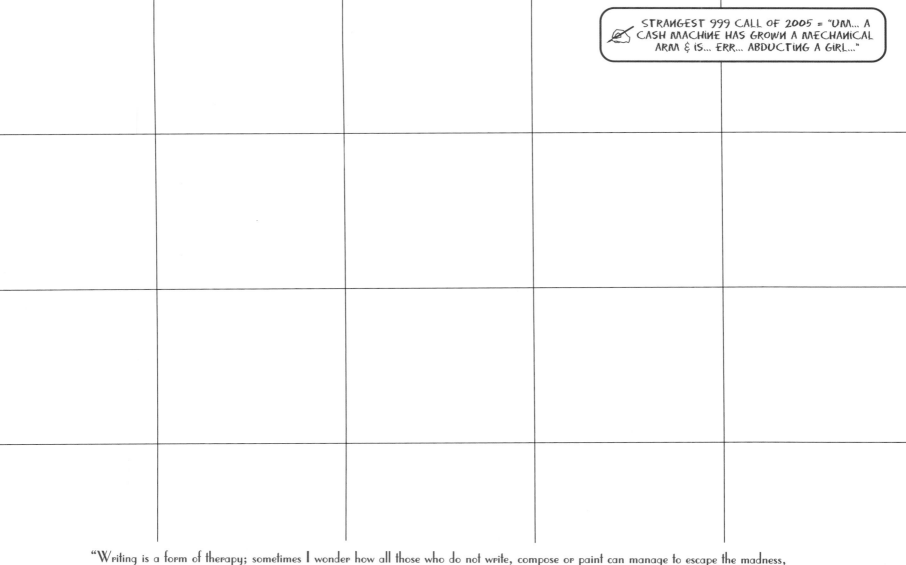

STRANGEST 999 CALL OF 2005 = "UM... A CASH MACHINE HAS GROWN A MECHANICAL ARM & IS... ERR... ABDUCTING A GIRL..."

"Writing is a form of therapy; sometimes I wonder how all those who do not write, compose or paint can manage to escape the madness, the melancholia, the panic fear which is inherent in the human situation." [Graham Greene - 1980]

THE GIRL WITH THE PIERCED
EARDRUM - BRISTOL - OCT 2014

53

Banksy Locations (& Tours) – Vol.1

– An Unofficial History of Art Locations in London

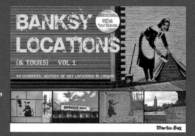

For 65 vintage London locations, originally arranged into three walking tours in Shoreditch, the South Bank and Farringdon, but now art history mainly, please buy my first book 'Banksy Locations (& Tours) – Vol.1'. It also includes street based art by Eine, Faile, El Chivo, Arofish, Cept, Space Invader, Blek Le Rat, D*face, and Shepard Fairey/Obey.

★ 180 pages / With over 125 colour photos

★ 5th Edition (Dec 2013) / ISBN: 978-0955471254 / RRP = £9.50

"BLT (Banksy Locations & Tours) is the new (unofficial) Banksy graffiti locations book, painstakingly compiled by Martin Bull.... I think Martin must have been a train spotter in a previous life – there's postcodes & GPS references for every location along with comments about the history of the piece or the things that have happened (hippies & strippers) when his tours have arrived at a site. It's pretty much Banksy all the way but he does include some other artists such as Eine, D*face & Blek Le Rat. It's a great little book, kind of reminds me of the little Banksy books (but a lot thicker). Ideal for reading in the smallest room in the house."

    www.artofthestate.co.uk

5 stars out of 5   "Are you a big fan of Banksy and got no plans this summer? Then this is the perfect book for you. A no-nonsense travel guide to all his London locations."
    Bookseller review by Lee Thompson, Waterstones Sheffield Orchard branch

"Don't buy this book, it's a little bit too much Banksy..."
    Review on You Tube by 'yourARTescortFRANKLY'

"This is the fantastic book that has become a cult favourite in the street art world. It is an ideal companion for anybody visiting London to see Banksy pieces in the flesh... don't waste time researching & printing maps. Grab this book & do it in one easy step. This book has sold out virtually everywhere, so this is an ideal opportunity to buy a slice of Banksy history."
    eBay seller who has taken his sales pitch slightly too far

Brand New Unwanted Gift. Great Book... Start off (bidding) at 99p
    a different eBay seller   (this made I larf! ☺)

Banksy Locations (& a Tour) – Vol. 2

This unique, unofficial, & unashamedly DIY book follows on from BLT 1 by rounding up the rest of Banksy's UK street based art from 2006 to 2010, as well as older survivors. It includes over 135 new locations, information, random facts & idle chit-chat, a full walking tour of his remaining work in Bristol, and also snippets of art by Eine, Faile, Inkie, Kato, Mode 2, BA / DBZ, & Rowdy.

★   382 pages / With over 230 colour photos

★   1st Edition (Dec 2010) / HARDBACK / ISBN: 978-0955471230 / RRP = £12.50

"...an eminently likeable book, full of down-to-earth humour and unexpected trivia."
    Venue Magazine – February 2011

"...a reminder of how far the nation's favourite tagger has come [and] an exhaustive guide to those subversive stencils and where to find them, with more than 200 photos and even a walking tour of Banksy pieces in his native Bristol."
    The Telegraph – January 2011

"Ellsworth-Jones writes perceptively about the "ethical dilemmas" created by Banksy's marketing techniques, yet still communicates the excitement of a "treasure hunt" for traces of his work in the scruffier purlieus of London' (*The Observer)*"
    Review of someone else's book, whose aforementioned treasure hunt unashamedly uses my books to fill a whole chapter of his book!

"This prosaic approach is refreshing in a book about street-art ... So, keen Banksy fan or merely mildly curious, this book delivers exactly what it promises: "...at the end of the day it's just a grown man doing what he enjoys in life" "
    Eye Magazine – January 2011

Away The Gas

– 50 years of utterly marvellous away game memories of Bristol Rovers fans

'Away The Gas' lets you wallow in 50 years of 'I was there' away game moments, from Halifax Town in 1963 to Pompey in 2014, and lets you find out just why Gasheads and Pirates (Bristol Rovers fans) cherish away days so much. The highs, the lows, the loves, the arguments, the times we got lost, wet or hideously late, and also the times we lay on a terrace in the lovely Spring sun, made some great mates on the journey home, or found the finest beer available to humanity in a tiny little pub. Written by the fans for their fellow fans, it contains 240 pages of funny, poignant and emotional short stories and tall tales, plus 16 pages of full colour photos.

★   256 pages / With over 55 colour photos & 15 Black & White photos

★   1st Edition (Oct 2014) / ISBN: 978-0955471261 / RRP = £9.99

Thanks & Acknowledgements

Obviously the real credit must go to Banksy (www.banksy.co.uk), and all the writers/artists who do their work on the street. Without them publishers would have nothing to show readers. Please support them, including any of their official publications.

Huge thanks to Matt Clarke who one day shoved a random colouring book under my nose, remarked it was good to do on holiday, and half-jokingly said 'Why don't you do a Banksy one?'. I dismissed it for a few hours but then my brain clicked and whirled and suddenly I was off on a journey to see if it was a workable idea.

Thanks to Stef who started this whole implausible publishing thing off in 2006 by asking me in one of those fuzzy Friday afternoon moments if I had ever thought of making my free street tours, location information and photos into anything more, such as a book? I had - great minds thinks alike eh? - but the original book mapped out in my head was about Eine's alphabet painted shop shutters in East London, not Banksy's street pieces. That is how Banksy Locations (& Tours) Vol.1 started. He also pushed me all the way through the process, and did all of the painstaking graphic design and put up with my perfectionism. After a lot of hard work BLT arrived and for the next few years he carried on helping me with anything related to Vol.1, gave me hints and tips whilst I wrestled with a follow-up volume, and even came back to design the cover of Vol.2. What a mug! But seriously, I'm genuinely not sure if any of this would ever have got started without him and I owe him so much love.

Many thanks to the veritable soul duo, Sam & Dave for various help with books, photos, locations etc. They are also members of the 'Class of 2006', who were there at the beginning, and continue to be there for me.

Thanks to all the people (especially Jason) who ever helped locate some of this art, or who even accidentally gave some info out. Particular mention must be given to anyone who contributes to flickr, especially the Banksy group, and above all the Banksy groups fellow volunteers; Mel, Ian, Quel, Jason, and Steve.

Credits

All photographs in this book (bar the three listed below) were taken by Martin Bull on the streets, after tracking them down or occasionally even being the first to 'discover' them whilst wandering or searching.

Thanks to Sam Martin (www.flickr.com/photos/howaboutno) for very kindly letting me use his lovely photos of the 'B-Boy' in East London (plate 32) and 'Vote Less' in Brighton (plate 44). I've never been to America but Michelle Robinson has and she just happened to take the photo on plate 28 for me whilst in New York, so I thank her for being there and reminding me I haven't.

The print management for this book was efficiently undertaken by Sam Martin @ TU Ink. TU Ink are specialists in managing print projects for Trade Unions so I am very happy to use them for my print needs and feel I am doing my little bit to help them continue to support Trade Unions. Long live Jeremy Corbyn as well. We'll be breaking into 'The Red Flag' in a minute...